BUILD

UNIVERSE

Ann Kathleen Edgar

I'm still me

© 2021 **Europe Books**| London

www.europebooks.co.uk | info@europebooks.co.uk

ISBN 979-12-201-1235-2

First edition: August 2021
Distribution for the United Kingdom: **Vine House Distribution ltd**

Printed for Italy by *Rotomail Italia S.p.A. - Vignate (MI)*
Stampato presso *Rotomail Italia S.p.A. - Vignate (MI)*

I'm still me

ACKNOWLEDGEMENTS

So many people to thank, I am overwhelmed at how much support I have received. Firstly, I would like to thank both my brothers George and Desi for having faith in your little sisters project you are amazing, I love you both. Thank you to Linda and Richard (it is what it is so it is) your long friendship has meant so much to me and walking with me on my journey in fighting breast cancer I couldn't have got so far without you both. Thank you to Medina and Chris for your friendship, laughter, and support you both are an inspiration in love, sincerity and generosity. Thank you also to Ula for your extrovert personality and keeping me positive, you're the best I am so please I met you. Thank you also to Amanda and Philip wherever in the world you have been traveling, your thoughts and love are also felt and are with me. Thanks also to Emily and Jo for bringing the laughter and friendship; you are also there when I've needed uplifting positivity, you both are a beacon of hope for all finding true love. Thanks also to Jane my shopping buddy for keeping me strong and grounded you get me and also thanks to Dee for letting me be me and for all the fun we have had an looking forward to more of that, Claire for your friendship our walks have been fully insightful and liberating, you are beautiful friend. To Tracy for your honest feedback, friendship and support. Thanks to Stephen what a laugh we have had and looking forward to catching up. To all my Ohana work colleagues for supporting my go fund page.

Special thanks to Dr Antony Neal and his wonderful caring, skillful team at BMI Mount Alvernia hospital St Martha's ward who over 6 years have become my second family, have cared, and treated me with utmost respect and genuine care, I survive because of all of you. To my breast cancer surgeon Mr. Adam Blackburn thank you for your expert skills in giving me back my self-esteem. To my editing team.

Finally, to my son, Ri just be you, you are wonderful and precious to me (I love you to the moon and back).

To all fighting breast cancer stay strong, stay positive have hope and live every day in the moment life is precious. Look to nature for inspiration and strength to keep moving forward.

Chapter 1 - No Fairy tales here

At the age of 6 my letter to Santa I asked for one thing. "Dear Santa, I hope I am not on your naughty list this year. I am sorry for not eating my peas and forgetting to brush my teeth and so so so sorry for hating bath time. I hope you can forgive me and keep me on your nice list as I have been really really good most of the year. I would really really like a Tiny Tears Doll. I promise I will love her so much and take very good care of her. Merry Christmas Santa from Holly Hudson. (I should have wished for a new Daddy as my Daddy was not a Daddy anyone would ask Santa for, or anyone for).

Six months later my older sister evented bungee jumping in the 70's. She attached a string to my Tiny Tears and launched her out our bedroom window. The string broke and my beautiful Emily hit the ground hard. Her leg was broken, her eyes were damaged she had a permanent squint. I cried for weeks and made a make shift hospital to aid her recovery. My sister told Mummy that I broke her on purpose and didn't take care of my toys. I was grounded for 2 weeks with no supper or treats. I hate my sister. (Sorry Santa)

The ground starting shaking, something was coming fast very fast. Glaring lights and the level of noise was deafening and blinding. I couldn't run, I couldn't move, I was stuck like a damsel in one of those black and white Buster Keaton movies waiting for her hero to come rescue her from the impeding train hurtling down the track, the menacing music growing louder, I'm struggling, wriggling to get free. The closed captions pop up as they do on screen in the movies "Help Help Help, someone help me" close up of my anguished face for dramatic effect. Where is he, its hurtling towards me, where the Fuck is he? No handsome hero no rescue Fuck! Fuck! Fuck! I'm fucked. "Miss Hudson, Miss Hudson, do you understand all what we said, do you have any questions"? The oncologist had stood up from her desk and her words were direct and brought me back into the room, her words were spoken as if read from an auto q, no compassion, no empathy, no understanding. I sat on the chair as I did as a child getting a scolding from Mother. "You stupid girl, how could you be so stupid and not speak up, do you know what you have done, do you know how much trouble you are in. You're always burring you head in the sand." Worthless, stupid girl, causing all this fuss you're not worth it, you don't deserve anything, your always in the way, you never listen, serves you right". Is she going to send me to my room with no supper? The tone of the oncologist voice was patronizing, humiliating, I felt worthless just as my mother told me before. I'm a child, worthless, in the way and underserving, I don't belong, and I'm not wanted. "Miss Hudson, do you have any questions", she repeated this time even more direct and intentional. Hell, yes, I have questions like, where was my handsome Prince Charming, he's coming right? I only heard a few words from the noise of the train like, Chemo, sickness, hair loss, surgery, possibly 2 years if I respond to treatment. The rest of the information came through like Charlie Browns teachers, wah wah wah wah wah undecipherable, just noise just sound no words. The oncologist's name

10

was Polly something or other, she did not give me hope, she did not give me sympathy or empathy she's the expert, is she right I'm I at fault did I deserve to get the big C. I've never smoked I don't drink; I eat healthy and exercise regularly, yes yes I ignored the lump longer than I dare to admit but I was scared frightened hoping it would go away. "Don't you value your life Miss Hudson she reprimanded; don't you know that by not coming sooner you have increased your chances of you not beating this". I want the ground to swallow me up now I want to get out of here I want to run and run and run. Life sucks. All this negative energy I will lie down and die, positive energy and I will climb any mountain point me in the right direction. Thank God I was reassigned to a very different Oncologist with a very different work ethic. From that moment on that day, I call that day Polly Long stocking whatever her name is day.

My BFF and I sat in our favorite coffee shop the one that sometimes celebrities come into. Last time the lead singer from the Jam came in for a coffee and sat outside drinking his coffee/tea. How strange the things that pop into our heads when facing death, "A town called Malice" playing over in my head, apt as I live in Woking Surrey, which I believe what the song is about. Oh, that's a good name for my Polly Long stocking, a doctor called malice. Huhmmm (Sorry Santa).

Chapter 2 — SO IT BEGINS

"Holly hurry up you are going to be late for school, you won't have time for breakfast", "Coming Mummy", I shouted back my voice carried downstairs to the kitchen. Where is it, where did I have it last? My Walkman can't walk to school without my music it's a half an hour walk. My sister growls at me from her bed hurray the fuck up and get out turn off the light and get out. She doesn't attend main stream school, the head teacher said she was slow learner, dyslexia is, as we now know the cause, it was never diagnosed properly in those days so pupils were sent to special schools for those who had learning difficulties. I'm the youngest of 5, 3 brothers, and one horrible sister, I never got over Emily's cruel fate, if she couldn't have what I had she would take it or destroy it so neither of us could have it. Even when she was older, she still adopted this energy I never learn, I never learn. She interfered in my marriage, slept with my husband stole my life.

I'm standing in front of our sitting room door just about to enter, "Don't go in there" my mother yelled you'll wake your father". "My Walkman's in there, Mummy I need it please I won't wake him, I'll be quiet, I'll be quick." "Ok, but if you wake him on your head be it you will be in your room for the rest of the year" she warned. I gently pushed open the door just a crack, the smell of stale alcohol, vomit and cigarettes hit me like a wave of toxic waste. OMG I can't have come from what I see lying spread face down on the sofa. Not a loving father, not the father that reads to you at night of prince charming and fairy god mothers, not a father who vows to protect you from the monsters under your bed or in your wardrobe, no ice-cream days out or father daughter bonding. No NO NO a drunken ex sailor, a disgusting man, who beats his wife and spends all our money on booze and betting on horses. I swear I will never ever be like him; I will never drink I will never be that kind of parent, parent what a joke he's not a parent not even a man, just a lodger that abuses and dictates to all of us. His house his rules, his way. Holding my breath, I spot my Walkman on the side board that's sits in the bay window of our 4-bedroom council estate house. I gently lift it and get out of there as quickly and quietly as possible, God he's so oblivious I don't think a lightning storm could wake him. I grab my duffle coat from the hallway coat hooks and head out the door. The door resists as the winter wind fights me to pull it too. The sound of the flag above bellows above as I head down the garden path. Head phones on I press play and as music starts Sheena Easton's words resonates through me and emerges me into a fantasy of wishing and praying to a god, I don't believe in that I can be that Modern Girl. Living my own life not relying on anyone but me, heading to the office instead of school, no pumpkins, no glass slipper, and no prince charming. "I won't build my world round no single guy; I am free to be who I want to be I'm a modern girl". Yeah right, it took me 40 odd years to get there. I took the hard path, or destiny took me that path to teach me lessons, perhaps. I never learn. One thing is true I had no guidance, no protection, and no self-worth.

Chapter 3 - DEAR SANTA

Six cycles so far and I've lost my hair, my dignity, my self-worth. The chemo is brutal just typical that I get a reaction to it, 80 percent of my body is burned like a chemical peel all over. So much pain. In the inside I'm crying and in despair, on the outside I'm showing courage and strength and yes, I've got this I'm going to beat it. How can I be anything else when all my friends and colleagues are rallying around and bringing me gifts and lifting my spirts with, flowers, chocolates (which I can't taste chemo takes away your taste buds), girls movie night in, Mr. Darcy in the rain "I love you most ardently". A few hours of escapism, forget my pain forget what I face tomorrow. I find the strength; I find the courage which like in Wizard of Oz you don't realize you have it until you need it. A heart, a brain, courage. Follow the yellow brick road Holly, find the Great Wizard you will get your ruby slippers. Click 3 times.

I feel like I've been in this tornado forever, never settling, never relenting. When I came back into reality after a doctor called malice day, I thought there was only two options open to me, one I was going to beat this and survive, two it was going to beat me and I was going to die like doctor called malice said two years or less. I didn't know there was going to be a third outcome. Fighting every day for years, 5 years so far to be exact. Treatment every 3 weeks, scans every quarter, this is what is keeping me alive, hope, courage, integrity, humility, gratitude. I'm still standing I'm still here.

"We have to get back home Linda, we have to get ready for Justin's 40th Birthday surprise, there is still so much to do before he gets back from New York". "You're still coming right "Oh Holly, surely we can postpone it till you speak with him and get your head around this, you are still processing it all you need to tell Justin and get his support". "No no not yet after, I can't cancel its too late, I don't want to spoil his special day". "I will tell him I promise not yet I need time, like you said to process it and give him the information carefully, properly".

As I look in the mirror at my reflection of how my body looks in my favorite LBD. I look hot for a 45-year-old, my boobs look amazing as always, this is Justin's favorite dress too. My breasts have always been my best feature, how can things ever be the same, how will Justin see me once they are gone. Will I ever feel this sexy again, will I ever feel like a woman.

The party is in full swing, Justin is in such high spirits despite turning 40. He looks so handsome; I was punching above my weight I thought as I approached him at a bar 3 years ago. Sexy, hot, charming yes prince charming, I love how he loves me. But I know him I know he doesn't handle this kind of news he still has an immature attitude to things; I don't think he will handle this news well, his favorite aunt died of breast cancer he's still hasn't got over it and now I've got to tell him his fiancée has to go through what his aunt went through. David his best man to be is staring at me, he walks towards me, and he knows me so well we have known each other since college. He knows when I'm not mentally in the room, he knows when my mind is elsewhere. "Hi darling, why are ya not dancin"? His American accent smooth, suave, cheeky. He's never had any trouble getting a date, a very typical chiseled handsome American like all woman swoon over in the movies. He's a top Lawyer, he just made partner with his firm this year, and he's a defense lawyer, very very good at his job. Well paid, sports car and a loft apartment to match his charismatic personality. "I'm just chilling sitting this one out, letting Justin take the lime light it is his 40th after all". "No No there's something up I know you Holly I know that look". I try to fight back the tears not showing my cards, holding them close, keeping my poker face till I have to put them on the table, showing my hand, showing the game is up, I don't have a winning hand, I'm bluffing. I excuse myself and head to the bathroom, David follows me to the landing. He can see I'm choking back the tears, "Holly what is it, tell me what's happened honey, why you upset is it Justin is he cheating on you, what's going on". "No, its fine it's not Justin I promise, I'm fine just a difficult day". "Holly, Holly, saved by the bell, "it's time for the cake Holly". "Ok thanks I'm coming". I start to head back downstairs, David pulls me back, "Holly what is it, what's happened". He's determined to get to the bottom of this, he hates to see me upset we have been friends for so long a strong friendship we know each other. "I have breast cancer David, I sob barley getting my words out, "I start chemo next week it's not good David". "How can I tell Justin this will break him he won't cope you know him; we know him. I have to be strong I have to be strong and let him see it's not doom, it's not the end." David grabs

17

me and puts his arms around me he also choking back the tears, "I've got you Holly, I've got ya, we can all get you through I promise we will all be here for you and Justin". "Happy Birthday to you", everyone's singing voices resonate all over the house as Justin blows out his candles, I go to his side and kiss him, "Happy Birthday JLove (my nick name for him, not Jlo but Jlove). "I love you too Holly Berry", his nickname for me as my Birthday is 26th December. "There's no place like home, there's no place like home". The wizard can't save you now Holly, the wicked witch is going to get ya.

Dear Santa I would like for this Christmas, a miracle.

Chapter 4 - I CAN'T SMILE

I pick up a Jackie magazine on my way to school. David Essex on the front cover, gorgeous just gorgeous one can dream. My school friend Michelle standing in front of the row of lockers. "Hey Chelle, what have we got first thing"? "Double Science", she groaned. "Can I double up with you Holly please please she begged, you know I hate Science". "Sure, Chelle long as Miss Courtney decides for us". We approach the Science block the familiarly smell of Bunsen burners and chemicals fill our noses, a smell that never never ever leaves you anyone whose anyone who had Science class will tell you. "Are you going to Rollerama this weekend Holly"? Michelle asked, "you know who's going to be there don't ya that boy you liked the one that looks like your favorite David Essex's". Simon Mason, ooooooh yes Simon Mason he was very cute and a good skater. Of course, I was going this Sat I've been saving my money to join Saturday's session. The roller-skating rink venue overlooked the seafront, as I entered the door the smell of skates, fried chips, fizzy drinks and sweaty bodies welcomed me the similar smell that you get at a bowling alley. I pay for my ticket and head up to the 1st floor to find Michelle. She was wearing pink t-shirt, and green corduroy trousers with leg warmers her curly hair tied in a ponytail. "Hey girl, look whose here she nodded towards the skating rink below. It was Simon looking dashing in blue jeans and a white T Shirt. I chose to wear my tight blue jeans shorts, my Wham T shirt and white roller skates with knee high socks, the wheels of my skates light up like those kids shoes you can get now that light up when you walk. Not bragging or anything but I have to say I was a pretty good at roller skating, I could skate backwards, spin on one spot do tricks and quite good a speed skating. Chelle and I head downstairs towards the skating rink butterflies in my stomach as I catch Simon's eye as he breezed past me standing at the barriers. Oh my gosh perfect the DJ started playing Disco Inferno perfect to skate to. Off I go Flash Dance on roller skates out to impress not the panel of squares as in the movie but Simon oh Simon I hope he's watching I hope he's watching. Simon is the first boy I allowed to put his hand up my top I was a very early developer when it came to my breasts, as I said my best feature. How those times seem so less stressful now, how I would love that all I had to worry about was handing my assignments in on time and working 9am to 3pm.

"Where are you going now Justin, I need you to help me filling in the insurance forms" I sounded a little dramatic and crazy loud, the drugs just affect me in so many ways at different times, unexpected and almost like an out of body experience that I don't sound or look like me, I'm morphing into Gollum from wearing the one ring to rule them all around my neck for too long. Yes, that's it that's exactly how I am finding out the side effects of Chemo and radio therapy, it is turning me into Gollum, an ugly version of something that used to be me, making me rage like Bilbo Baggins if I anyone dares mention how I am or stay strong you can beat this for the 10 thousandth time. Justin's slams the door on his way out and I cower under my rock talking to myself, "my precious, my precious".

"Hey Darlin, it's only me", David called out. He insisted to have a key so he could come in and check on me while Justin's at work and help with cooking or anything I need. "What's up with Justin, he nearly ran me over in the drive way"? "He's got a big case he's working on very high profile it is keeping him working late at the office, I hardly see him but I can't help but think he's secretly happy he has a legitimate reason to stay late and not come home to me, his wife who now looks like Gollum, no hair, pale skin not the glamorous full breasted sexy fun dancing woman he married. "Jesus Holly your sick girl cut yourself some slack he understands that he knows he loves you no matter what". "Does he, David I don't think so, it's how I predicted, I feel I'm losing him David really". "He won't touch me he can hardly bear to look at me, I'm not angry I understand I knew he's not the kind of man to cope, we are arguing all the time and when we do talk it's as if I'm in the court room with him answer yes or no to pre written questions." "I'm sure honey it's not as bad as what you imagine the meds, they can mess with your head the doctor told you what to expect". "Have you eaten breakfast yet, I bet you haven't eaten, let me fix you something, you need to keep your strength up girl, you need a David New York special". He winks and smiles that American smile that all the girls swoon over. I nod and smile and say, "Sure Mr. Native New Yorker, I'd love that."

As I sit curled up on our velvet sofa with a blanket wrapped around me, David sits down to the piano and starts to move his manicured hands over the ebony and ivory keys. He starts to sing, "You know I can't smile without you. I can't smile without you. I can't laugh and I can't sing. I'm finding it hard to do anything you see, I feel sad when you're sad. I feel glad when you're glad. If you only knew what I'm going through I just can't smile without you. Happy tears fill my eyes and I do indeed smile, how can I not, my college pal, the song I sang on Karaoke night, the night we met, we have been best friends ever since. I keep his ego in check and he keeps my pessimism in check. Oxford came alive for me when he came, the long nights revising didn't seem such a chore when you had David to lighten the load and studying breaks, he made sure the time was used to the max for enjoying and reviving our souls. All the students especially the pretty blondes all flocked to David's term parties. Such great times such times of hope, change the world, and change the future. He skillfully transitions into a Barry White, "You to me are everything". Everyone loves a bit of Barry.

I didn't hear him leave as I had fallen asleep during his rendition of Endless Love. A blanket now covering me that was I assume was placed over me by him. I wasn't sure but I am pretty sure that there was something on his mind other than his dream of becoming the next Lionel Richie, serious I'm sure but decided now was not the time to tell me. My instincts were right he told me a few days later that he had to return to New York he had family business to deal with. In my selfish self-wallowing, I forget sometimes that David has a whole other life in America, I've come accustomed of having his friendship and attention to myself. "We can Skype every day if you need it Holly, I'm here I wouldn't leave you if I didn't have to you know that right". "Of course, David don't be daft, I will speak with Justin and Linda will come by and check in on me don't you worry I will be ok, the treatment is working I'm heading in the right direction now the doctors are really pleased with the outcome."

I will miss him, I will miss him terribly.

Chapter 5 – FLAWLESS

It's been almost 10 months now and I seem to have got my Christmas miracle early, the effects of the one ring that rules them all has worn off, I am in remission I am in cloud nine. Santa, I love you, you jolly jolly old soul. To top it all off my breast reconstruction has gone absolutely amazingly, my breasts are as good as new, yes there are scars and radiotherapy scars but I have cleavage again after so long I no longer have to wear prosthesis in my bra, praise be to cosmetic surgery, praise be to breast care surgeons. I can now go buy actual pretty lingerie again, YES, YES, YES. Justin has been in France for the past 3 months on a case defending a man accused of murdering his wife, I've never seen him more excited about a case. "It's like the fugitive Holly, Harrison Ford a man accused wrongly this is big girl, just like the movie, this will make me Holly". I'm happy for him this is what he studied for this is his dream job it's all he ever wanted to be, I try and push aside the fact that he's gone to France with his pretty blonde admin. Nope I can't it's there, the feeling won't go away and it consumes me and I go crazy and call Linda to meet me for coffee so I can have a Bridget Jones rant and reassurance that it's all in my head and Justin would never ever cheat.

After 3 more coffees and blueberry muffin later, I head down the high street and stop dead in my tracks outside Marks and Spencers and head toward the sexy lingerie range. Ted Baker sexy red and black set with matching suspenders and stockings, Justin arrives this evening I will surprise him and remind him how much I miss and love him and revive our sex life.

As I look at myself in the mirror, I choke back the tears as I recognize the woman I used to be, the sassy woman staring back at me come back from the brink, strong, sexy I am woman.

I decided to keep them on and throw on my over coat and as I leave after paying, I step out on to the crowded streets among all the rest of the Christmas shoppers rushing around to find the perfect gift and all along I smile secretly to myself that little does everyone know that underneath my over coat is a woman who has her sexy back. A new lease of life and new zest, grateful and thankful that I'm alive and as I board the bus the snow starts to fall and life is full of hope again. Magical, thank you Santa x.

As I turn the key to our terrace London town house I can hear music, gosh Justin is home early. I push open the front door and rush in with such excitement and happiness I didn't notice the woman's red coat and Mulberry handbag in the hallway. You know when you see in the movies or TV those scenes where you watch and you know what's going to happen and you're waiting for the reaction of what the actor is about to walk into and they are so good at their job that you actual feel every second of the scene unfold, you feel it, you feel it real even though you know it is acting. WELL, here we go this is one of those scenes, they are both naked on the sofa, yes, the same velvet sofa I lay as wretched and sick.

The music is so loud and they are so engrossed in their act that they don't notice me. I'm unable to move I am frozen in shock at the scene in front of me not believing what I'm seeing. I'm discovered she jumps up and all I can think is how beautiful she is, perfect skin, perfect pert breasts, perfect body size, perfect glossy blonde hair, perfect teeth, did I say perfect breasts, like seriously perfect. She is FLAWLESS.

Chapter 6 - NAKED

I was eight when Mummy made us join the Brownies at our local church hall. All in all, I enjoyed it. It was at this point that I started to compare myself to other girls. How they look, how they dress, how they behaved, their background. As I nervously entered the hall wearing my second-hand brownie uniform minus the yellow neck scarf, bow whatever it's called, frankly I didn't think it really mattered oh but little did I know it mattered. I noticed that some people things seem to be effortless whatever they did or wanted. Sally Newman was one of those girls. So, there are very pretty girls, symmetrical lines, posh clothes, posh voices, they would receive a Barbie for Christmas not her poor 2nd cousin Cindy. Daddy would fix everything. In those days instead of there's an app for that they had parents for that. The kind of father I wished I had. When I would ask my Mummy why we don't live there or have that, they have it all she would say but they have everything they are not truly happy they haven't had to earn it, you have to earn your way in life if it's handed to you on a plate then you don't learn life's lessons, you don't become a spoilt brat. Of course, I was too young to understand what she really meant the real truth. I began to understand at that age there is a hierarchy, the thing was where did I fit in to this line up. And there is the first lesson I should have learned, the key is not to fit in but to be the best version of myself, be true to me and not how others want or slot you into where they want you to be so they stay high up in the lineup. I would lie in bed at night and try and work out why some people when they start off in life are given a compass to guide them true North, a stable boat, a capable crew and provisions for the journey. They navigate the seven seas going through life with effortless ease and dreamy pleasures and views and safe harbors. Me on the other hand I seem to have been given a broken compass, a boat that leaked from the start, no crew, no help, bare essentials for provisions like corned beef and spam. How I'm I supposed to navigate my way safely through life naked and afraid hurtling towards the eye of the storm with no compass or adult guidance. It wasn't till later in life endurance, resilience, integrity not giving up pushing through no matter what always looking to the horizon for dry safe land. I often think of the explores of old setting out to seek new land of opportunity if they had given up even after days, weeks months of no land in site how many times did their resolve get tested and if they had given up, places, new discoveries where would we be.

So here I am again face to face with my insecurities, self-doubt, those voices in my head, you're not good enough, you're not worthy, you'll never be flawless, youthful, desired. His pretty EA had now left without any signs of shame or remorse, in fact I'm pretty sure she's happy its al out in the open. I can barely look at Justin as he pulls on his t-shirt and sweater. I can no longer choke back the tears, no longer choke back the emotions, "Is this what you want Justin, flawless skin and perfect young ample breasts with no reminders of Cancer, no longer desiring me your wife of 13 years, the wife who loves you no matter what, in sickness and in health till death do us part.

I take off my overcoat, I no longer feel how I felt in the store staring at my reflection, I no longer felt empowered, wholesome again, bounding through the streets with vigor for life to proudly come home to my husband to be held and desired, to feel sexy again to feel just to feel. "Look at me, LOOK AT ME JUSTIN, what do you see, do you see your wife, the wife that has stood by you and loves you no matter what, or do you just see Cancer Justin is that all you see me as your wife who has Cancer, do you see me, DO YOU, WELL DO YOU!" WHAT DO YOU SEE"? I push and shove him to try and get a response any response. His silence spoke volumes and the look on his face, well he didn't need to speak, I would have given anything for him to break down and ask for forgiveness and tell me that he loves me, that I'm his world, I'm his everything, that he sees me that he made a mistake, that he sees his HollyBerry. I would, I know I would have. I love him still. Tears streaming down my face I know I've lost him, "I'm still me Justin", I'm still me". My voice is faltered and broken, defeated shamed and naked for all the world to see. Broken, lost at sea, no compass, no way to navigate away from the storm. "Holly, listen I, I I I didn't mean fff". "Get out, get out, get out, GET OUT" I screamed and pushed him towards the door. "GET THE FUCK OUT". I slam the door shut behind him, and I feel he's still waiting there on the door step hesitating, hovering as if waiting for some sign of absolution, I hear his steps fade, my legs give way and I crumble to the floor, unbearable pain, my heart and resolve shattered in seconds. "I'm still me I sob, I'm still me".

I'm not sure how much time had passed while I lay shipwrecked in the hallway. I peal myself to standing position and head to the bedroom and sit on our bed, facing our wardrobe mirrors. The woman in the reflection staring back at me is unrecognizable, not the same feeling as I got when the Cancer drugs took their toll, a different unrecognizable. Cancer was breaking my body; Justin broke my heart. The photo frame on the side table of the day of our wedding, I remember that moment as if it was yesterday, how happy life was, the future looking bright, shining like a diamond. Full of sparkle, enchanted love story, my happy ending. The images come to life like they do in the Harry Potter movies, memories gone by, reliving that moment in time.

[Chorus]

Once I ran to you (I ran)

Now, I'll run from you

This tainted love you've given

I give you all a boy could give you

Take my tears and that's not nearly all

Oh, tainted love

Tainted love

What, really Marc Almond standing in my bedroom belting out the chorus to tainted love. Really, REALLY, stop stop STOP, stop singing.

Sometimes I feel I've got to

Run away. I've got to get away

From the pain you drive into the heart of me

The love we share

Seems to go nowhere

STOP, STOP, STOP I pick up the photo frame and hurl it at the band, just missing Marc's head. "ENOUGH ALREADY"! "Alright love, alright this is your imagination projecting a broken heart not mine", pun intended". The band disappears, but the words of the song are still ringing in my ears.

I change into my running gear, I admit Marc Almond is right I have to run away, I need to get away. I take my normal route heading towards the park, music loud in my ears to drown out the last hours. I jog past a couple on park bench, eh what I'm seeing things, its them, Justin and pretty blonde naked, arms wrapped around each other kissing they see me and smile and laugh. WHAT THE F........., I look again a normal couple chatting over coffee and sandwiches. I carry on and there's a gardener leaning against a tree chatting to a young woman, its them again naked, wrapped up in each other kissing and looking at me at the same time laughing, staring. This is crazy, I'm crazy everywhere I look I see them both, the ladies pushing their pram, other joggers, dog walkers everyone everywhere they are tuning into them naked laughing, her flawless pert breasts her youthful physic. I now here we go Marc Almond is back. Really!!!!

Don't touch me please

I cannot stand the way you tease

I love you, though you hurt me so

Now, I'm gonna pack my things and go

Tainted love, oh, tainted love, oh

Tainted love, oh, tainted love, oh

Touch me, baby, tainted love

Touch me, baby, tainted love

I stop to take a break on the bridge, still everywhere I look, every person is them naked, laughing, kissing, touching, the scene is playing over and over and over. I turn to run back home and not looking where I was going, I bump into a couple sightseeing, I fall backwards on to the hard ground, stunned for a second, I hear her voice, "Oh my, are ok, are you hurt?" She bends down and offers me a hand, it's her naked her perfect round breast right in front of me, no scars no imperfections, Justin's choice, Justin's choice over me. He wants youth and beauty not middle aged and heading south. He wanted escapism from endless hospital appointments and uncertainty, he wanted a future of celestial bliss with this Angel, this vision escapism from sickness, he wanted freedom. I shut the door behind me, I jump in the shower and let the water drench over me wishing it could wash away the past 24 hours, wash away the Cancer, wash away the heartache. I miss David, I miss him more than ever.

Chapter 7 - LETTING GO

Someone once said Wait for no one, walk your journey, you're in control of you own destiny. I thought I was on my journey, I thought Justin and I were on our journey together. The house seems bigger, empty without his belongings, without his favorite things. My world revolved around Justin like the earth orbiting the sun. Without his light I thought my world would die, sucked of oxygen and light and love. How is it that we find ourselves relying on someone else's compass to guide us through the storms? I am human and need to be loved just like everyone else does. I remember every Easter and Christmas when The Wizard of Oz would be televised and we would sit in our front room the only time a family would come together for one purpose, for escapism from our realities that we wish we could change. I understand now that you don't realize you have courage until you find you need it, just like the cowardly lion it was in me all along I only knew till I needed it. Facing Cancer, facing life without Justin. The values we learn as children from our parents, life, they shape us but they don't have to be our values when we are older, we can change those mind sets, I am good enough, I am worthy of love and abundance, I can change and shape my own future. So that is what I decided to do, to learn the art of law of attraction, inviting in what I need and want to manifest into reality. I have the tools there all along, life and negative energy talk us out of the thing we wish to achieve, even our demons whispering you'll never make it, too much competition, one in a million chance, like winning the lottery. I decided to take back control, I make a mood board and things that I've always wanted to do but put on the back burner because of fear of failure, fear of what people would say of my aspirations and dreams. I've always been good at art, it was one of the subjects that I really looked forward to at school but was a subject girl like me I was told would not succeed in, typing, admin, secretarial was the direction my careers teacher pushed me towards. Don't get me wrong I was good at it I could type 60 words a min, I should have learned piano. So, I clear out the garage and turn it into an art studio and I enroll in my local art class. I love Monet and Picasso and visit the art galleries at weekends for inspiration. Forward 2 years and I have my first art exhibition scheduled for this weekend. Dec 3rd.

David's communication became less frequent and video calls were postponed and rescheduled. Life is going well for him in New York, he's living his dream and on his own journey. On a normal Sat as, I was visiting an art gallery and bumped into an old friend of Justin's. She told me he was engaged to be married, you guessed it to Miss Flawless. I was standing in front of a Picasso at the time. I would love to see what Picasso would paint for that moment, when you think you are over the hurt and pain and BOOM, just when you thought you had let go the wounds reopen and you are left feeling just like a Picasso painting. Deconstructed, surrealism, symbolism of a life, I wonder what people would see in my life in painting, would they see it as a Picasso. The great experts in the field of Art, analyzing, and critiquing. Well, I guess I will find out this weekend. In my late 20s I visited a tarot reader, she told me that later in life I would go through a difficult phase and in order to find my ten of cups my happiness I would have to let go of the past. Past hurt, past relationships, let go of the baggage, but there is always something there to remind me. Dragging me back to negative beliefs and self-doubt. Let go of people around you that don't have your best interests at heart, energy stealers, dream stealers, raining on your parade. Take control, it's your journey your life and even if you fail then try again, you're here one day gone this next and you have to have diligence, determination, dream big, be your authentic self. Make myself happy. I understand now, I wish like people said go back with the knowledge I have now.

Chorus:

She don't build her world 'round no single man

But she's gettin' by, doin' what she can

She is free to be, what she wants to be

'N all what she wants to be, is a modern girl

The signs were all there, woman older than me were already learning the lessons and finding. their independence and empowerment. It's being going on for centuries.

Letting go of yesterday, letting go, no more punishing myself for past decisions. Dumbledore was right it's not our abilities that make us who we are its our choices. I choose to let go and use my internal compass to guide me, it was there all this time I just didn't see it. Fragile but free. It's not so hard to realize I'm human after all.

Chapter 8 - FREEDOM

But today the way
I play the game is not the same, no way
Think I'm gonna get myself happy I think there's
something you should know
I think it's time I told you so
There's something deep inside of me
There's someone else I've got to be
Take back your picture in a frame
Take back your singing in the rain

George Michaels Freedom lyrics are resonating around the gallery, as people check in their coats and head upstairs. These people are here to see my work, these people are taking the time and have come to evaluate, critic or enjoy my work. Yes, my work, my whole life depicted on canvas. The highs the lows, the happy the sad. All in large print for all to see. Determination, diligence, drive, resilience, freedom.

I bought a new LBD for tonight; Justin's favorite LBD went to charity of course. Classic Audrey Hepburn style, I feel great, I look great. My art work seems to be being received well according to the gallery owner. "Holly darling, fabulous, fabulous, these pieces are amazing". Marcus the gallery owner he's so flamboyant, with a purple jacket and black shirt and tie, extremely well groomed, always immaculate. He introduces me to his partner Pierre, air kisses all round. "There is a very handsome man who has just bought one of your pieces. The piece named transformation. American accent if I wasn't already in love with Pierrer, I'd be buying him a drink".

David, he was dressed in a blue suit very sharp like one of those men in the fragrance ads. I stood and watched a while hardly believing he's in the same room, I want to rush over and throw my arms around him and let out all of past emotions. But before I could he turns around and makes eye contact and smiles that beaming smile that melts hearts. "Hey Holls you did it you made your dream come true your very first gallery showing, I'm so proud of you girl". I put my wine glass on a waiter's tray and threw my arms round him and held him tight. It was so great to have my best friend back here in London where I need him, I so missed him. As I embraced him, I could feel his toned torso and he smelled so great, sexy. How come I never noticed this before, I never really seen David as other woman see him, he's always been David my rock, my go to man, but tonight there's something about tonight.

Wow this is a tough crowd tonight, what is going on, normally the crowd are buzzing and cheering with my renditions. Jeff the pub restaurant manager is staring at me and making hand jesters implying I'm losing my touch and do to do something quick. God, I need this job with waiting tables, playing piano and singing is getting me through college. Oh no its him that egotistical American friend of Justin's he's heading my way. He

40

grabs the mike and whispers in my ear. "What really, you can't be serious this crowd won't be into that". "Trust me darlin I know what I'm talking about". "Ok, ok but if I get fired, I'm coming for you". He's a typical example of handsome, an attractive male leading actor. Agreeable to the eye to a correct taste, a pleasing appearance and expression, attractive, very attractive.

"Start spreadin' the news, I'm leavin' today
I want to be a part of it
New York, New York

The crowded pub goes wild, as this dashing young American breathes life into this tough crowd. God I actually have to swallow my pride and admit he was right; God his already overinflated ego will be even bigger he won't make it through the door. I roll my eyes in defeat and give in to the chorus and join in. Not surprisingly he has an amazing voice to go with those chiseled features of his. All the woman in the pub have maneuvered themselves right up close to our make shift stage dancing flirtatiously in front of David, a native New Yorker.

The art galleries downstairs bar lounge is beautifully and tastefully decorated, I wouldn't have expected anything less from Markus.

Modern, contemporary clean lines exquisite lighting, something that you would see in an interior design magazine. David sets down my drink on the marble topped table. French Martini, my favorite he remembered. "You ok kiddo, you seem nervous, are you concerned about your art, because seriously there's no need to be your work is amazing really really amazing, I'm so proud of you Holly". "No no, I'm fine honestly I'm happy", ooooooh my god what's with my voice, I sound like Mickey bloody Mouse. I reach for my drink and I know it flying the contents spilling all over David's trousers. What is wrong with me I can't seem to get my words out why I'm I feeling awkward and nervous it's David, like its David. As I'm apologizing profusely rambling like giddy teenager as I try to wipe him down with a napkin, my hands shaking and can't quite make eye contact. He takes my hand and reassures me its accident and joked he'll send me the dry-cleaning bill for his Hugo Boss suit. Every fiber in my body reacted to his touch in a way I have never felt before, David has taken my hands in his many times and comforted me during my Cancer. No time have I ever felt anything like this before not even with Justin? As he returns to the bar to replace my spilled Martini the realization of what just happened dawned on me, OH MY GOD now I see it, what all the woman over the years have been seeing when they look at him, I see it now, Oh Shit, Shit Shit I'm in love with my best friend, I'm in love with my native New Yorker.

Chapter 9 - PRINCE CHARMING WHO KNEW

Prince Charming - a fairy tale character who comes to the rescue of a damsel in distress and must engage in a quest to liberate her from an evil spell.

"Once upon a time, long, long ago a king and queen ruled over a distant land. ... They named the baby princess Snow White, but sadly, the queen died after giving birth to Snow White. Soon after, the king married a new woman who was beautiful, but as well proud and cruel." Richard my best friend Linda's husband was reading a familiar well known bedtime story to their 6-year-old daughter Emilia. He has her full attention as always and hung on his every word, even though he has read the story of Snow White many many many bed times. I realize now that I'm older that it's not necessary the story that captivates the children, no it's the importance of who is reading the story. I believe Richard could have read the sports page and Emilia would still be captivated. It was time, precious time spent with her father who she adored, he was her Prince Charming. "Again, again she implored" with saucer cat like eyes hoping to hold all his attention for as long as she could before she had to fall asleep. This is something I observed that I never once experienced during my childhood. My father was very rarely sober he wasn't the kind of father that reads bedtime stories, tuck you in at night, and make sure there are no monsters in the room. No, he was either drunk, in the pub or betting shop or sat in front of the television set waiting for the racing results. Mother was too stressed and busy holding things together trying to feed and look after 5 children and a useless husband.

Because my Birthday fell in Dec, I didn't start school till the following Sep when I would have been nearly 5 years rather than starting school like most children at 4 years. I learned to read myself, fend for myself. Often having to wait for anything that would filter down from my elder siblings. Usually having to settle for left overs or scrape the last of the butter from the tub. My brothers would buy weekly comics of the time, The Beano, The Dandy, Buster. I had to wait till they were absolutely finished reading any of them before I would ever dare to touch them. I would watch while they giggled and laughed at the pages and was jealous that the comics did no yet make me laugh as I hadn't quite learned how to read. But boy when I did when it clicked it was like a whole new world opened up. I used to just look at the pictures and characters in the comics and not quite understand the stories therein. Now I could laugh and understand the jokes and follow the stories week from week and I was even more eager for my brothers to finish reading. Having to fend for myself most of the time as a child, an original latch key kid, who when I came home from school let myself in, make the fires, clean the dishes, peel the potatoes all before dinner and then whatever time was left to do any homework or assignments. Reading for me became my escapism till American cop shows came on telly, and love for 80's pop music. Having parents that were not the normal tactile, expressing feelings or I love you and reading bed time stories meant that I had to learn most things myself although my brothers did teach me a few things, like chess, playing cards, cricket, golf, riding a bike etc. Most children in the 70's, 80's for sure you would find dictionary of sorts or atlas in their school bags. Early ones would have picture to help describe and explain the word, there was no google or Alexa then. Seems in most fairy tales that the women were most princesses that got the happy ever after, pretty houses, pretty dresses, even Cinderella was originally a princess from a rich family until her wicked step mother. So, my imagination and fantasies that I would retreat to I would be someone else, lived somewhere else and had the beautiful life that the Princesses had in the stories. No matter how many times or how hard I wished upon a star happy ending never seemed to appear, at least until Justin, or so I thought but that as we know did not end happy ever after. Maybe they should end the stories, And Prince Charming and Snow White have a beautiful wedding and have a chance to live happy ever after, (if they communicate well, don't break their marriage vows, go to marriage counselling, and sign a prenup) oh and make sure that Prince Charming's secretary is not young pretty blonde and flawless. Maybe just maybe they will live happy ever after. I know, I know I sound bitter but honestly, I'm not really nothing wrong in having hope and manifesting your dreams, that's what drives us hope the chance for happiness and peace of mind. I think those are the things that should have been top of my list to Santa. Now I replace the Santa with the word Universe and write my gratitude list and send out my list of the things I wish to manifest into reality. It's not all about wishing upon a star you do have to put in the work and set your intentions and go towards it you have to be hungry for it, resilient, genuine and with a good heart. My life revolved around Justin, I fitted my world around his, his goals, his life path and put my dreams and ambitions on hold as I loved him, I was happy that he was happy and that at the time all that matter, I would have continued making him smile for the rest of my life, if it wasn't for destiny or universe or whatever name you have for it deciding for us. This was not my life path and I realize that now as my internal compass has kicked in and I head in the direction to my true happiness, guiding me finally true North.

Chapter 10 - SANTA BABY

I love Christmas, I have always loved Christmas that's when my belief in something better will come was always at its best, wishing that Santa will bring you just want you asked for. Beautiful Christmas window displays, lights, Christmas trees, Christmas music. These days some would say that Christmas is no more than an orgy of consumerism, and that the message of Christmas has been drowned in a frenzy of competitive present-buying and consumption on an almost obscene level, that the generosity and hospitality and the true Christmas message has got lost in Translation. Perhaps in part some of this is true, but for me I soak it up every year, the Christmas adverts, the Christmas movies that play back-to-back from the month of November. It's not because my Birthday is also at Christmas to be honest as you expect that sucks a little but as I got older, I just embraced it and make sure I celebrate it especial after my Breast Cancer diagnosis it makes you really appreciate that you have been blessed to reach another Birthday and Christmas. You change your priorities, and you count your blessings. I see Christmas as in the eyes of Charles Dickens, I love A Christmas Carol, and it's always been one of my favorite books. As the Cratchets in Christmas Carol, we as a family were not rich, we lived pay check to pay check, my mother would save on the catalogues at the time, paying weekly throughout the year to try and give us the best Christmas she could and we were grateful for Turkey roast a meal we didn't have often to us it was a luxury. We had no Christmas crackers or many frills and we often made our own Christmas decorations and had to be careful each year with our tree decorations that were fragile and brought out every year. Mummy never let us touch any of the decoration, lights or baubles and some were given to her by her mother and like I said they were glass and fragile and she didn't trust us so tree decorating was always her task every Dec. The tree had to be decorated exactly in the correct sequence every year, the best baubles to the side of the tree that faced to the outside along with most of the heavy string lights, she was very particular and under no circumstances where we allowed to touch. The threat of slapped legs and no supper, we did as we were told no matter how magical the attraction the tree became.

It's been three weeks since the Martini incident with David. I threw myself into my work as the Gallery showing proved to be very successful and commissions started to come forth. Since Justin left, I have been having anxiety dreams, the same dream usually. The day of my diagnosis I walk out the hospital entrance and you know those videos that everything is in fast forward and there is one person standing still or moving normal speed, right that's me and then in the corner of my eye I see some figure coming towards me in black, then they split into two, three, four multiple figures and as the draw closer I recognize them. It's the guy from the Matrix, the agent, agent Smith that chases after Neo. Yes, that's him oh my god there are loads of them like in the movie heading towards me from different direction coming to get me. In my dream I'm running and dodging each one as they try and grab and I fight them off. Cuts to different scenes, in woods, along a river, top of a building, on a bridge, I come to an edge with a water fall below and I'm falling and falling and into the water I go and I sink under and I feel like I'm drowning unable to breath I start to struggle and then I feel someone grab me and lift me out of the water.......it's David, David saves me from drowning, David saves me from Agent Smith, which on reflection I'm guessing he represents cancer cells attacking me, thousands and thousands of Agent Smith's menacing and aggressive, relentless just like in the movie. Is David Morpheus, to explain that I can beat the Matrix, I just need to reach the Oracle find the answers and be free from the Matrix to be free from Cancer? Gosh I wonder what Freud would say, he might have agreed with me if he saw the Matrix lol. I think David would be flattered to be compared to Neo or Keanu Reeves for that matter. Before the Martini incident it was usually Mr. Darcy that would save me, or dashing Sinbad from those amazing movies I sat glued to as a child fighting mutant monsters created my wizards and sorcerers. I don't believe I need saving like Cinderella, Snow White or some other damsel stuck in a tower by a handsome Prince. No, I believed I was and am strong enough to keep getting back in the ring like Rocky and running up the Philly steps and smashing it. I think I just need a soft landing, a warm hug, someone else to take a few of my plates I'm juggling, peace of mind. I think back before David left for New York, that day when I woke up with a blanket pulled around me when I fell asleep while he sang Barry Manilow. He was caring, genuine, beautiful, and thoughtful, he knew exactly what I needed. He is the perfect gentleman, Prince Charming right in front of me all this time.

"Think of all the fun I've missed
Think of all the fellas that I haven't kissed
Next year, I could be just as good
If you check off my Christmas list"

Eartha Kit's voice purring through the gallery bringing me back to that Christmas Karaoke party, Justin was working late on a case and David insisted I go and dragged me to this amazing quirky little pub. He put my name forward for Karaoke and he chose Santa Baby as he said my voice is ideal for that song, he said you have a great voice Holly this song shows it off really well, sexy kitten, slinky just like Eartha prowling across the stage. It was one of the best nights I remember we laughed so much and talked and talked about everything and anything and the time just whizzed by and I felt I could trust and tell him everything. My shadow side, my venerable side any side no judgements no long-winded analogies as Justin used to do that was so patronizing. Deflecting from the real answer, deflecting from talking about actual emotions, used to drive me insane, "Would you just tell me how you fucking feel, just once tell me how you actually feel". Not if this cup was a train and this salt pepper was you blah blah blah OMG.

Don't get me wrong I loved Justin I really did but as in most marriage there are times when our partners little ways irritate us a little more than we expect.

"Hey Pussy Cat". David appeared right in beside me I was so lost in my head I didn't even notice him come in. "You free for lunch Hol's", "Surely even famous artist gets a lunch break, right". He winked and beamed a proud smile as if this is my famous artist friend and I want to treat her for lunch. "Yeah yeah, we artist get lunch". OMG there I go again, Mickey bloody mouse voice, what's wrong with me. "I'll just go get my things", I nervously back up and give a salute as I gingerly walked past him towards the social lounge. WHAT is wrong with me jessssssssssssss it's David, it's just David you've had lunch with him a hundred times what's so different about today. He looked at me with his hands in his jean pockets head tilted to the side and gave a peculiar quizzical look as if at any minute I was going to run round the gallery like Kevin in Home Alone waving my hands in the air and screaming hysterically.

The cold air hits my face as we step out onto the crowded pavement of Christmas shoppers and business men and woman. David hails a black cab and opens the door and gestures me. "Where shall we go"? "I have an idea, do ya trust me"? "Always", I reply. He whispers in the driver's ear and the cab pulls away. David is dressed in jeans with brown shoes, blue shirt and waistcoat and camel overcoat, with a wool college type scarf. His mousey brown hair is styled as if he just walked out of a high-end salon, or as if he was about to take part in a photo shoot, and he smelled divine, intoxicating to the senses. He was chatting away about what he got up to in New York and even though I can hear every word I wasn't really paying attention I was too busy imagining him naked, his toned

51

tanned body standing behind me, we are in a luxury hotel with panoramic views of the city, I can feel him behind me, he gently pulls my hair aside and kisses my neck and electricity shoots all over my body, every fiber in my body brought to life as if Frankenstein himself had just pulled the lever. He artistically moves his hands around my body caressing my breasts. Ever since my breast reconstruction no man has seen or touched them since. I push out the memory of that day standing in front of Justin after purchasing the sexy lingerie to celebrate the results of my transformation from my very talented skilled breast surgeon. I turn to face him now and I am now totally ready to surrender, surrender and let go of inhabitations and fears that I'm not good enough, let go of self-doubt, I deserve abundance and love and happiness. He lifts me up and my legs automatically wrap around his waist and we kiss and move our hands exploring each other with such urgency and melt into one person one entity of passion and wanting and longing as if the world was going to end.

The black cab comes to a sudden stop and David and I are thrust forward slightly, a cyclist had pulled out and cut up the driver. He sent out cursing words and hand gestures of anger of the idiocy of the cyclist. "Do ya have deaf wish mate"? He turned to David and singled the £20.80 on the meter. David paid with tip and we excited the cab. He took my hand to steady me out of the cab as Mr. Darcy with Miss Bennett alighting from a carriage. Just the touch of his hand was enough to make my head spin and lose my mind. Now I long for a kiss from his lips to warm my soul and I will surrender myself over to the possibility and ecstasy of love.

Not much has changed, it still has that nostalgic feel, and black and white photos hang on the wall of all the movie and Hollywood greats. The tables have changed and rearranged and with different lighting but all in all its how I remembered it. David had brought me back to the quirky restaurant that Christmas when I sang Santa Baby. "Oh my God David this is awesome, I can't believe you remembered and brought me back here, how wonderful, you are such an old romantic". The waiter escorts us to our table where Humphrey Bogart is hung on wall above along with James Dean and Maureen O'Sullivan. The piano is still in the same position over in the corner with a view to all the restaurant tables. We order drinks and peruse the menus. "Perhaps you should stick with water Holls, as these are my absolute favorite jeans", he teased, as if I need reminding of our last meeting when I drenched him with Chambord liqueur infused cocktail. "Very funny I retorted, you're safe," I assured him, "I'll set it well away from you, I promise no dry-cleaning bill will be needed". I say that, but inwardly I'm as nervous as hell, like a love sick teenager on her first ever date, the effects of my earlier day dream still tingling throughout my body and mind. Time goes by in a hurry too quickly as always spending time with David always uplifts my soul and spirit, his positivity, charisma and infectious laugh resonates all over the restaurant, attracting attention from other diners. Everyone notices David when he walks in a room ever since I've known him, I never used to fall under his spell to the attraction and pull of his effortless charm. I understood it but to me David was David. Now though, it's as if like Snow White I've awoken from a sleeping curse, and I've woken in a fluffy land of fairies and unicorns. I like it, I like it a lot.

The waiter gives David some sort of signal with a nod of his head, and David stands up. "Right Hulls how's your singing voice these days, do you feel your inner Eartha dying to get out?" "David no no I can't, I can't, it's been ages ". "You'll be fine, just like last time, I'll play piano and you sing, easy, come on, ITS C H R I S SSSSSSSSSS T MAS", he urged it his best Noddy Holder rendition. "Ok, ok let's do it. David very quickly gains the attention of our fellow diners and introduced me, the well fed and liquid fueled dinners were intrigued and animated, partly of course to David's personality and good looks.

Think of all the fun I've missed
Think of all the fellas that I haven't kissed
Next year, I could be just as good
If you check off my Christmas list

The diners and staff all their feet clapping and cheering and many thank you'd for making their lunch festive and memorable. I miss how an appreciative audience makes me feel, I'm also now in high spirits full of Christmas magic. David stands up from the piano and pulls me towards him and wraps his arms around me with a warm and generous hug. He pulls a way and our eyes meet and yes you guessed it, I'm totally in my fluffy enchanted world, and without any hesitation I move forward and kiss him.

Chapter 11 - WALKING ON THE MOON

"No peeking now HollyBerry". Justin had me blind folded for an unexpected surprise, a 20 min car journey later he helps me out of our Range Rover, correction his Range rover. He guides me through, doors and steps and then I feel we are back outside as the warm summer nights breeze hits my face and he brings to a stop and turns me to face the way he wishes. "Stay there don't move, don't take the blind fold off just yet till I tell you". "Ok, ok, I'm excited to find out, I love when Justin is passionate and enthusiastic and full of surprises. I love how he loves me. "Alright you can take it off now", he announces. As my senses come back inline, I take in the scene unfolding, Justin is down on one knee, he has a small box in his hand inside a beautiful diamond ring, his face beaming with pride and anticipation and a certain level of nervousness. There is a beautiful decorated table behind him set for two with Roses and champagne waiting to be appreciated, candles and rose petals surround the table in a heart shape and glass jars hang around this gorgeous immaculate roof top garden lit up with tea lights. I realize where I am now, its David's Loft apartment roof garden. "YES YES, I scream with delight and joy". Finally, he has popped the question, "I WILL MARRY YOU!" He gets up from his kneeling position and we throw our arms around each other and kiss, he places the ring on my finger, I'm complete I'm happy, happy happy.

David appears from the roof top entrance smiling and clapping and congratulates us both. He walks over to the table, grabs the Champagne and pops the cork with an extra element of theatrics. A few years later I found out that most of the romantic flare for the proposal mostly was down to David. I had my suspicions as I know that's not Justin's forte, he's facts, figures, academic not romantic although he has his moments, what he lacked in romantic ideas he more than made up in the bedroom department, definitely had no complaints there.

"The colour and texture is unique and inspiring, it's a beautiful piece, the artist French". I can feel Markus's eyes boring into the back of my head as he listens to my very poor description of one of the galleries most impressive pieces, (aside from mine of course ;). The couple nod as if in agreement but obviously I can see they are not impressed with my lack of information and passion to sell it, they retreat to the far side of the gallery, they are retreating away from me. Markus marches quickly past me in pursuit hoping to salvage any hope of regaining their interest, his expression as he passes was to say the least not a pretty one, his eyes wide with disbelief at what he just witnessed, mouthing WTF.

I head to the gallery bar and order a latte and sit by the window staring out to the river and Christmas shoppers browsing the Christmas huts all lined up with their unique foods, Christmas beverages and crafts, like bees around honey. It's Christmas and what is playing at present throughout the gallery is "Walking on the moon", I roll my eyes and sigh there's always a song to reflect every situation, like when you change the radio channel in your car to avoid that song that reminds you, broken hearts, childhood memories, embarrassing moments you'd like to forget, and each time each song reflects what you're feeling at that very moment. As if the universe itself is making you face reality, reminding you that you can't hide you have to face it sooner or later, just rip the band aid off and be done.

The kiss, the kiss, the kiss, oh WOW the kiss. I know its cliché but his lips did taste of wine and I loved it and wanted to stop the world and stay in that moment. I replay the moment over and over and over again trying to decipher his reaction, did he enjoy it, was he kissing me back or was it all me, it's all so foggy, his phone rang and he broke free from my arms to answer and next thing I know he's apologizing that something has come up and he has to leave. I search his face for any sign of reassurance of what had just occurred, that he wanted to kiss me as much I wanted to kiss him, that it was mutual, did I read it all wrong, did I just make the mother of all mistakes. Bloody fluffy, fair, unicorn world, why why did I go there.

It's been 3 days, it's now what's called Christmas Eve Eve, 23rd Dec. No phone call, no text message no WhatsApp message. I was a lunatic checking my phone every 2 mins which didn't go unnoticed by Markus.

"Ok WTF is wrong with you missy you're acting like a crazy lady?" Markus demanded as he plopped himself in the chair opposite. "Oh, Markus I'm soooooooooooooo sorry, I know I'm just going through some stuff." "Spill, tell me don't' leave anything out, I still want to have a gallery in the New Year". He ordered us a couple of Christmas drinks and leaned forward with anticipation, Markus can be on the dramatic side and at times he holds. Back his inner diva at the gallery, his gallery is his pride and joy he's worked very hard to get where he is and he is professional by day and diva by night, but in occasions like this I appreciated his dramatic inner diva as he won't hold back and will listen intently and sympathetically, no judgement, reassurance and friendly advice of what he thinks you should do.

"Darling, it's David, he won't make it awkward for you, trust me just talk to him, call him, just make it casual tell him you'd like to meet up and swap Christmas presents, you got him a gift right."? "Yes of course," I replied. "Well then you can judge for yourself, if he doesn't want to mention the elephant in the room, if he sides steps it, or you never know he probably is feeling the same way as you do."

You've been friends for years Holly he's seen you at your absolute worse, he nursed you through Cancer for Christ Sake, its David were' talking about, he's a gentleman straight out of a Jane Austin novel. And just as he said that a text came through, and the decision was made for me. He asked to meet at the Crypt Café at St Martin-in-the-Fields, Trafalgar Square. A self-service cafe underground, brick-vaulted church crypt with gravestones and sometimes on Wednesday they have jazz. When I first told David about this café he thought I was pulling his leg, as an American he just lapped it up he loved it we met there quite a few times after, he loved the idea of eating around all that history. It is the perfect place if you're looking for somewhere quiet to sit and work or have a small meeting. He wants to meet at 1:00pm for lunch. Just enough time for me to pop home and grab his gift.

Giant steps are what you take

Walking on the moon

I hope my leg don't break

Walking on the moon

We could walk forever

Walking on the moon

We could live together

Walking on, walking on the moon

Seriously this song is haunting me, the taxi driver is obviously a fan as he raises the volume up and tries to copy the iconic drum rifts. I ask him to wait while I pop into my flat and grab David's present from under the tree.

Some may say

I'm wishing my days away

No way

And if it's the price I pay

Some say

Tomorrow's another day

Original brick-vaulted ceilings and historic tombstones lining the floor provide the backdrop to David's unexpected lunch invite. Walking into this hidden and welcoming lunch venue to meet David as I have done on several occasions doesn't seem to give me quite the feeling as before. I could be facing walking out of here without my best friend or as the lyrics of the song still ringing in my ears, I could be taking Giant Steps Walking on the Moon. I really do hope it's the latter as I truly wish that David and I, we could walk forever, walking on the moon.

Chapter 12 - TURNING BACK THE CLOCK

"Oh, now, now, now, now, now, just a minute. You must understand, my dear: On the stroke of twelve, the spell will be broken, and everything will be as it was before."

There's always always a catch to every fairy tale right, to make the readers or viewers believe that all hope is lost and the beautiful princess will not get her happy ending. If I was Cinderella, I might have been tempted to say, "You're a bloody Fairy Godmother with a magic bloody wand, what kind of fairy are you anyway that you can't extend time or stop the clock let me party all night long, I've been cooped up slaving away. But then I'd probably seem ungrateful and risk being turned into a toad. Cinderella goes through heart break and mistreatment and she teaches us not to give up on our dreams, if there's any chance to set things right, I simply got to try. I simply can't lose David as a friend over a kiss. I can't let this effect years of wonderful genuine friendship.

David left the restaurant that day as if the clock struck 12 and everything was going to be as it once was, the black cab would turn back to a pumpkin and the driver back to a lizard and the cyclist would have the last laugh.

During the cab journey to The Crypt, that day played over and over again in my head and every day since. Constantly turning back time in my head and rewriting how I would have liked it to play out.

We can't physically turn back the clock, but isn't it strange how, music, food, smell, all our senses, bring us straight back to the past quicker than Santa's sleigh. For many of us, snow is synonymous with Christmas. ... We are more likely to see snow between January and March than in December. Watching all the Christmas winter advertisements on TV, or old music videos such as Shakin Stevens, Merry Christmas Everyone, always transports me back to Christmases of my childhood. Growing up in the North of Ireland we were pretty much guaranteed snow Christmas Eve or many days before. I would wake up early excited with anticipation that Santa had brought me what I asked and wished for, the scene outside, the silent blanket of snow that had fallen during the night would make even the bleakest places look and feel beautiful, magical. You can't hear the snow fall, but I always felt it, like a celestial presence passing through leaving their magical blessings. When you're a child you wish for the time to pass quickly, you want to be older, grown up, now I wish to stop time or wish for more time. When the sun finally came up, we would grab our winter coats, knitted hat and gloves and dash outside to build our snowmen and enjoy a snowball fight and forget all about time itself, becoming lost in the magic of Christmas and the free gift of snow to play. Mummy would call us indoors for Christmas lunch our fingers and noses frozen, but that was all part of making the most of the fun of snow while it lasted before it melted in to slush. Our humble Christmas dinner would be divided into 7, homemade paper chains and table decorations made at school adorned the table. There was usually a fight to who got the wish bone so we could pull it apart and make a wish.

Later in life I googled the tradition, and apparently the tradition of breaking the wishbone did not originate in America. It dates back to an ancient Italian civilization called the Etruscans. Then the ancient Romans adopted this custom and then passed it on to the English in the 16th century. Then the English took it to America where this custom is celebrated for thanksgiving. Anyways I don't remember many of my wishes coming true no matter how many wishbones I got to break, but the thing with traditions is they shape our childhood and our values. Some traditions are lovely and memorable some not so.

The Crypt gets very very busy this time of year, especially lunch time, I spot David on the high tables with the high stools, next to one of the pillars, thank God I wore a trouser suit, a vision of me doing a Miranda and falling off the stool and every one staring and laughing and capturing my wounded pride on their phones to share it to tick tock accounts, insta, or share across every social network, RUDE! He's taking a call on his mobile phone, spots me and smiles his usual welcoming winning smile (this is a good sign I thought to myself). He gestures me to join as he asks whoever is on the other end of the line to hold for a sec. My first thought was how on earth does he get a bloody signal down here, he must have taken Kevin Bacons advice on 5G or whatever he advertises, I don't know it's all marketing blurb technic to me, but I could never get a signal for sure.

David is suited and booty as they say, in a dark suit, Hugo Boss or Tom Ford, definitely one of those designer brands, he looks sexier than ever. I can't breathe, I can't think I feel like I'm at a final interview to see if I get the job or worse a disciplinary interview and the setting is quite fitting as we are located in a crypt with readymade graves. YIKES! I should have suggested another venue, fluffy unicorns seem more appealing right now. David seemed reluctant to discuss whatever business he was in the middle of on the phone in front of me and made hand signals that he had to step outside the café walls just outside the gift shop to continue his call. I held up my hand to indicate it was ok with me. Perhaps I can take the time to make a secret plea to our spiritual ancestors and manifest a successful outcome or spiritual advice.

"No matter how your heart is grieving, if you keep on believing, the dream that you wish will come true". I looked up and Cinderella was sat right where David was just sat. Cinderella, really of all the spirits you send Cinderella, she's not even a real person she's fictional. "If you'd lost all your faith, I couldn't be here. And here I am!" I was hoping more for a Fairy or Someone with a magic wand at least or someone that could turn back time. I need to get more sleep or counseling. "When there is kindness, there is goodness. When there is goodness, there is magic". OH MY GOD, STOP IT, STOP IT. I need to get out more. I noticed that David had already took the time and queued for food before I arrived and had ordered me exactly what I would have gone for, Soup of the day with focaccia bread, and a bottle of still water. Another good sign I hoped, clutching at any sign that all is fine and we won't discuss any elephants in the room, which is what I was more or less hoping, no elephants so far, only Cinderella who was now busy clearing tables, you can take the girl out of the cinders, but you can't take the cinders out of the girl. She just can't help herself. If Snow White and Seven Dwarfs show up, I'm checking into to the nearest Priory clinic. David returns, I search his face for any indication of disappointment, any sign of awkward body language, I'm trying to spot and compare any behavior differences from past lunch dates today, before this first meeting after the.... I Kissed David Day.

Chapter 13 - STRAIGHT OUT OF A DICKENS NOVEL

"Gaily they ring

While people sing

Songs of good cheer,

Christmas is here.

Merry, Merry, Merry, Merry Christmas,

Merry, Merry, Merry, Merry Christmas.

A small group of carol singers had entered the Café, all of the diners welcomed this festive cheer, the singer's angelic voices echoing around the brick-vaulted ceilings and walls, the traditional joyous celebration of song. This is a very hard song to sing, my vocal range can't quite manage the high notes, now as I sit and listen waiting for David to finish his call, the carol so beautiful sung by a group dressed in costume straight out of a Charles Dickens Novel. I love when people go that extra mile to bring cheer and goodwill and uplift our spirits, I really need that right now for sure, I'm hoping the carolers singing voices will up lift David too.

"I took a guess and ordered you soup, I hope that's ok darling, if not the queue has quietened down, I can go grab you something else if you prefer." His voice was steady and light no faltering over words or awkwardness. "Look listen Holl's, I I I em about", and before he could continue and interrupt with a croaky voice, "I brought your Christmas gift", I lift up the gift bag containing a perfectly wrapped present, I love wrapping I find it therapeutic and again nostalgic. "Awe hey that's thoughtful and lovely of you, organized as always, I have something for you too but I haven't brought it with me". "Organized, it's Christmas Eve Eve David", I tease. I don't know about everyone else but I have yet to meet a man who is totally organized before the 24th December. "Holl's about the other day" he continues. "This soup is really spicy but I like it I like it," "HOLLs please let me explain, please", he implored with Puss and Boots eyes. I let him continue, rip off that plaster get the pain over with in one fell swoop.

"I want to apologise for the way I have been lately, spooking, ghosting or whatever the young'uns call it these days." "Gosh I don't know how to tell you this it's awkward, embarrassing, I'm afraid I would hurt you, betray your trust." What, what is he talking about, certainly not the kiss, he thinks he owes me an apology? "David wait, no it's me that should be apologizing, I crossed a line I got caught up in the music and nostalgia of the venue, how it meant to us as friends." "Holly wait wait please, you don't' understand I didn't run out of the restaurant because you kissed me, I ran out embarrassed as I didn't feel I deserved such a flattering move, the kiss Holls it did take me by surprise, but a welcomed and lovely surprise, I have been wanting to kiss you like that since we first met." Oh my God I was not expecting this, oh my gosh he loved it, he enjoyed the kiss all this time I thought I crossed that line between friends. "Holls, the person I was speaking to on the other end of the phone, he hesitates for a bit wondering what my reaction is going to be I guess, he looked fearful that I'd be angry, disappointment, I don't know but I realized I was holding my breath I was forgetting to breath with all the tension of how out conversation would play out. "David why I would be upset with you, you can speak to whoever you like I don't understand". "Justin I have been speaking and spending the last few weeks with Justin", he confessed, "but Holls I swear it's not what you think I'm not taking sides what he done to you is unforgivable and trust me Justin was the last person I wanted to reach out to after what he done, after what he put you through, and that day at the restaurant that's the reason I was behaving uncharistically, I was ashamed, embarrassed keeping it from you I wasn't sure how you would react, that you might have thought of it a betrayal to our friendship". "I swear Holl's the moment I met up with him the first thing I wanted to do was punch the guy I swear I could barely look at him."

Gaily they ring

While people sing

Songs of good cheer,

Christmas is here.

Merry, Merry, Merry, Merry Christmas,

Merry Christmas

The carolers had circled the café right back to near where we were sitting. Their voices sounding more and more harmonious, my heart was beating fast and I couldn't get any words out and I suppressing tears that what to come flooding to the surface, tears of relief, tears of Christmas Joy and happiness.

David went on to explain why he needed Justin's help. David comes from Scottish decent; his great Aunt live in Edinburgh and he explained he came back from New York as her estate was under threat, apparently there was some legal issue to the deeds and right to the large estate and property after her husband passed away. David adored his Aunt Annabella. She practically raised him after his parents died in a tragic car accident when he was just 9 years old and was pulled from his home in America to be raised in Scotland with his aunt and Uncle. He met Justin when he moved to London and they became the best of friends. "I hated to admit it "he continued but Justin is the best god dam defense lawyer I know, and he knows the history of my aunt and Uncle's estate which saves valuable time than explain and going over everything with someone new". "David, David please you don't have to explain or feel that you betrayed our trust, God David", before I could stop myself the words just came spilling out like a volcano of lava, before I was dormant and not wanting to speak or face the truth, no erupting unexpectedly, an explosion hot lava words that's too late to stop. "I love you, don't you see I love you I didn't see it before because my world revolved around Justin's and don't get me wrong at the time I was happy making him happy, but after I recovered from my broken heart I realized I had put all my dreams and ambitions on hold, and when I'm with you it was the only times that I felt I could be myself." "You were there for me at my worst and my best." "All this time David you were right in front of me from the moment we met, I was too afraid to lose you, too wrapped up in building my life around Justin's. "You're my best friend and I'm truly truly madly in love with you."

All the cards are on the table, I was so engrossed and lost in this surreal moment I didn't notice that David had got up from his side of the table and was standing right next to me. I turn on my chair to face him. His gorgeous blue eyes, the colour of beautiful tropical blue seas that you just want to emerge and lose yourself in. He reaches up his hand and tucks some stray strands of my hair around my ear and cups his hand around my cheek and back of my neck and pulls me close, the aroma that emanates from him is intoxicating, keeping eye contact his lips meet mine the spell is broken and I fall into the beautiful abyss of magical enchantment where dreams really do come true.

Where is Cinderella anyway, I want to scoop her up and spin her round and take a selfie. If you keep on believing, the dream that you wish will come true. I am going to have that quote printed out and framed as an affirmation and gratitude that I am now a believer I am now in a magical world of unicorns and fairies. "God Bless Us Everyone".

Chapter 14 - LET THE SUNSHINE IN

Christmas Eve morning and the winter sun is starting to shine through the large windows of David's beautifully converted spacious loft apartment. I can hardly describe how I'm feeling right now, as the images of the night before replay in my mind as I lie awake naked facing David and memorizing every inch of his face and upper half of his naked body. Like Bridget Jones waking up to her Mr. Darcy watching him while he sleeps as if this moment is a dream, one does not wish to wake from. If I am dreaming, I wish to stay here in this moment stopping time and soaking up this wonderful life I now find myself in.

Remember my day dream in the cab, I thought that dreams like that would not be the same in reality, not in a million years would I have dreamed of how true true love, unadulterated love and passion. With Justin we were two worlds, two worlds that revolved around each other, mine revolved around his more than his with mine. But last night, and I know it may be cliché but two worlds became one. We blended and melted into one person, our confessions of how we finally felt about each other unleashed in a love scene from the movies, the romantic music playing out to each move of our hands and bodies. The intense moment where we would stare into each other eyes lovingly holding each gaze, discovering each other for the first time, exploring our sexual needs and desires taking turns and giving each other time to find out what would give the maximum feeling of erotic pleasures that pleased us the most and committing them to memory so we can learn to master our technics, to make it last, to lose ourselves in our personal sexual pleasure time after time, losing ourselves till all time is forgotten and we give in to sleep, until the sunshine comes in.

We decide to leave the Café Crypt and head to a nearby pub for Christmas drinks as the Café would be closing soon. We had so much we wanted to say, now that our true feelings had been unleashed. I opened up to David about how Justin's action made me feel, how I retreated in a cloud of low self-esteem, self-doubt and self-sabotaging. That he no longer saw me, that after the effects of all the treatment I was still me. I told him all about standing in front of Justin in my carefully chosen lingerie that he only saw the scars, as if sifting through the debris from a shipwreck, items washed up on the beach that you can sort of recognize what they once were and which part of the ship they belonged to, and you grieve for loss of the broken processions that you once treasured dearly. I was debris from the storm, a casualty of the brutal storm of Cancer Treatment. The Storm I faced, the storm I survived, washed up yes but I found the strength to pick myself up from wreckage and found the strength to step forward with hope, resilience and determination. I survived, I'm a survivor, powerful and Justin's couldn't see it, he just couldn't see it.

We had managed to grab a neat little booth tucked away upstairs, the pub was tastefully decorated, modern classy. I could see David was choking back tears as he listened my story of pain and lost at sea. Because of the booth we were able to sit right up close and personal our hands caressing each other from time to time of love a reassurance and acceptance. "You know kiddo, in Japan, broken objects are often repaired with gold. The flaw is seen as a unique piece of the objects history, which adds to the beauty". No, it's my turn to choke back tears. He continued before I could respond to this beautiful realization of his perception of me.

"For me I have always seen your beauty Holl's, from that moment I saw you playing piano and losing the crowds interest." "Oh God don't remind me, I seriously thought I was going to get fired, I sucked, if it wasn't for your New York rescue I'm sure I would have lost my job which I needed to get me through college".

"Hey Frank always gets the crowd up and going", bring out your inner Sinatra".

The pub is buzzing with Christmas punters enjoying a Christmas Eve drink before heading to their homes and preparing for Santa's arrival.

"Holl's there's something else I haven't told you". OK it seems to be an evening of truths. "Go on I'm listening." I'm distracted by the nape of his neck, dam how did I never noticed how sexy he was before, now I'm discovering that the slightest moves he makes drives me crazy with want and desire. The crowd was whooping whooping as David and I finished the song with style and finesse. I reluctantly admit that I appreciated his intrusion for saving my job. "No problem, any time." We unintentionally head in the same direction towards the bar. Justin is has already got in a round of drinks. "So, you meh meh meh met my young American friend Holly. I met Justin the week before and he bought me a drink and we chatted in-between my sessions. There was a certain attraction to Justin, always well dressed, studying to become a lawyer he spent long nights he said over his legal books. Highly intelligent, cute rather than pharwwwwarrr I say yes please. David confessed that he was immediately attracted to me, he wanted to know all about me and was genuine in his intentions to date me. As the night played out, he said he realized how smitten Justin was with me and as a true gentleman he backed off as he knew how difficult Justin found catch a break getting a date. He didn't have as much charisma and charm as David. Although smart and attentive, I found his vulnerability alluring and cute. Looking back, I believe the demands of his job changed him as he got closer and closer to his goals and dreams. By that time, we had already fallen to the innocence of love and hopes for the future and where our dreams were going to take us. We had a beautiful wedding, family and friends wishing us well for the future, Justin and Holly perfect couple, made for each other. I often wonder if we had have had children would things have been different. I always thought Justin would make a wonderful father, I think it would have brought back to his own childhood and nostalgic memories. It just didn't happen for us, long hours at the firm and materialistic purchases of expensive cars and interior design.

David as I now know was sitting in the wings lovingly admiring me from a distance, but secretly wishing he was more than friends but he would never have made any advances even when Justin and I's marriage went through moments of stress and uncertainties. Would I have left Justin for David if I had known at the time? I very much doubt it as I said I was in love with Justin and for me my wedding vows were a promise not to be broken, sickness and in health. David would never had betrayed his best friend in such a way, you don't sleep with your best friend's wife end of, and you just don't. That was David, loyal, dependable and trustworthy. Underneath all that bravado was a guy longing to be with his true love but having to go from one unfulfilling relationship to another without depth or purpose without commitments, he compares everyone to me they just weren't you Holl's, no one gets me like you.

"Hey you", Hey you I replied. David is awake, busted he caught me staring while he slept. He liked it, he liked that finally as he said in his own words, "You're my soul mate Holl's" I will always love you; I will always see you for who you are, beautiful, strong, amazing, sexy, you to me are everything, sexy did I say sexy". I loved when he quotes of sings Barry White, who doesn't like a bit of Barry White. He maneuvered himself on top of me with great stealth, and worked his way down his lips caressing and kissing with urgency and passion, we made love, and again and again, and the winter sun shone through windows as if acknowledging this union, rising and shining in sync with our every touch and movements.

"Hallelujah", let the sunshine in!"

Chapter 15 - HAPPY EVER AFTER

The scene was set, a beautiful garden setting, open white wedding tents with greenery garlands, white roses and fairy lights framed around the tables and chairs set for 30 guests of close friends and family. I chose an elegant simple off-white ball gown with a side slit on one side and my hair was curled and pinned to perfection. Completely opposite of what I wore when I married Justin.

Markus came into the room and threw has hands to his face in excitement and choking back tears of joy, he came towards with air kisses, "stunning, stunning Holly you are beautiful, David is a lucky man". "I'm so proud to be walking you down the aisle". "Thank you, Markus, you look pretty dapper yourself".

David proposed on New Year's, we were on a boat on the Thames waiting for Big Ben to strike its iconic bells, and for the fireworks to light up the night sky. David got down on one knee just before midnight and proposed. The next few months to come I had moved into David's loft apartment and we started planning the big day. It came to the time of choosing the wedding guests and who we would invite. And in case you are wondering Justin will not be getting an invite.

This is it the moment when the princess gets her prince after defeating their foes and breaking enchanted curses. I never dreamed I could be this happy, that I never dreamed I'd be the one who would get this kind of happy ever after. Like in all the fairy tales of old I now was walking down the aisle to my Prince Charming. My best friend, my world. Que the doves and Disney music, and hand out the sick buckets.

When Justin and I got married, at the time I believed it would be forever that you only get married once. I also believe we have many people come and go in our lives playing a part in this game of life.

Attending my quarterly scans, I know longer suffered anxiety dreams the night before, I no longer feared the outcome as I was maneuvered into the scanner. David was with me, David was waiting. I can't tell you the difference between facing Breast Cancer alone compared to having a loving supportive man to guide and hold you tight till the storm passes and you were safe again in the arms of his safe shores.

When you are in alignment, when you are living in harmony with who you truly are. Pointing directly north you feel a sense of comfort, ease and flow. One thing that I've learned from my ongoing battle with Breast cancer it brought me to a point where I had to stop and listen, listen to my inner compass, meditate, to be mindful, to go with the flow, raising my vibrations to positivity, to connect to the Universe. Bringing focus back to me. It's about being presence in the moment, needing to heal. Learning mindfulness helped me listen to my inner compass. We are given the tools right from the start they are within you. My ship is now safely back to shore. I sail down the aisle to safe harbors. David, a lighthouse shining out his endless love guiding me to the happy ever after. I am safe in the sanctuary of all that is David. The dark shadows that once followed me are vanquished by the light of his beautiful love for me. I know I've always known that no matter what future we face he will always see that I AM STILL ME.

Contents